Collins



Adheres to National Education Policy

PREPARATORY STAGE

# SUPPLEMENTARY BOOKLET 3

*Enhanced*

# Science Now

Series Editor | Jyothsna Natraj

# About the STEAM Activities

In the 21st century where the world is rapidly changing with sudden disruptions and unexpected real-world problems, being skilled in just one stream may not be enough. Many real-world problems can be solved only through interdisciplinary approach. Moreover, educationists have been emphasizing on the importance of subject integration and cross-curricular links. **Science**, **technology**, **engineering**, **arts** and **maths** (**STEAM**) education is one such approach where the integration of these five disciplines is utilized to solve real-world problems. Through this approach, a variety of skills such as critical thinking, creativity, innovation, communication, collaboration and entrepreneurship can be applied to make the students ready for the future, where these skills would be applicable in any field of study.

Students need to be introduced to STEAM education early on in life while their mind is still full of curiosity and imagination. STEAM education would not only help in producing tomorrow's designers and engineers, it would also help develop innovative mindsets and the ability to solve real-world problems. This would bring the students one step closer to becoming innovators or creators, not just passive consumers.

This supplementary booklet which comes along with ***Enhanced Science Now*** series, aims to introduce STEAM education to students from classes 1 to 8. There are two problems, based on ***real-world contexts***, in each booklet. The contexts have been carefully designed and mapped directly with the syllabus of each class. The students would be applying interdisciplinary concepts they have learnt in a class to find solution to the given problems. With each problem, research tips have been given to help in the initiation of idea. Clear directives have been given for students to identify the problem, research and record data, record their thinking, sketch their ideas, make observations and improve their design or solution as they work through creating the design or solving the problem.

We hope the students, while applying the concepts they have learnt to solve the real-world problems, would find their learning meaningful and thus be inspired to become future problem solvers, critical thinkers, innovators or inventors.

Content Developed by Excelsoft Technologies Pvt Ltd.

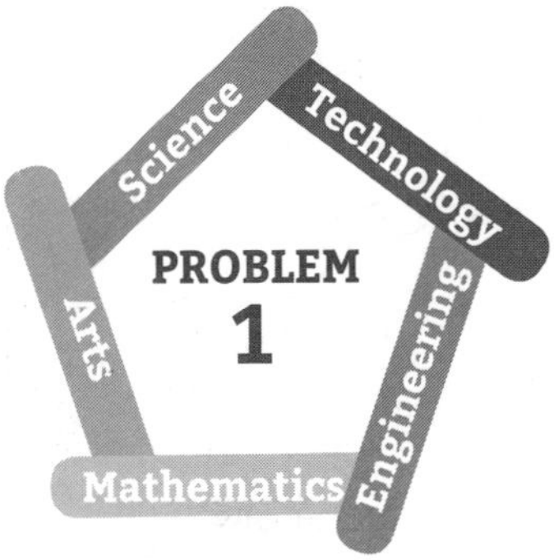


Rizwan and his friend Ram read about solar system. They decided to collect information on solar system and construct a small model of solar system. Help Rizwan and Ram design and make a simple model of solar system.

**Statement of the problem:**

____________________________________________

____________________________________________

____________________________________________

____________________________________________

____________________________________________

**Research tips:**

1. Solar system
2. Planets
3. Sun
4. Orbits

**Gather information relevant for this problem.**

1. ______________________________
   ______________________________
2. ______________________________
   ______________________________
3. ______________________________
   ______________________________
4. ______________________________
   ______________________________

**Draw/Sketch your design.**

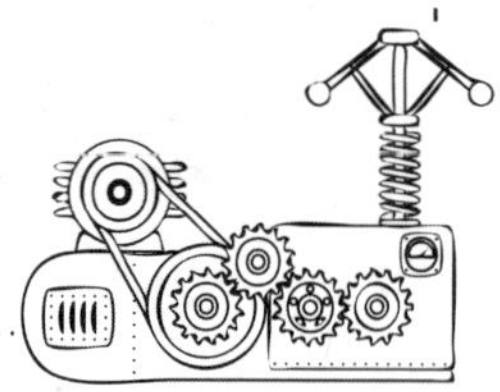

**Materials required:**

______________________________________________

______________________________________________

______________________________________________

______________________________________________

______________________________________________

**Construction (Write down the steps to build your design):**

1. ______________________________________________

______________________________________________

2. ______________________________________________

______________________________________________

3. ______________________________________________

______________________________________________

4. ______________________________________________

______________________________________________

**Implementation of the prototype (Try out your model):**

Step 1: ______________________________

Step 2: ______________________________

Step 3: ______________________________

Step 4: ______________________________

**Observation (What worked? What did not work?):**

______________________________

______________________________

______________________________

______________________________

______________________________

**Scope for improvement (How can you make it better?):**

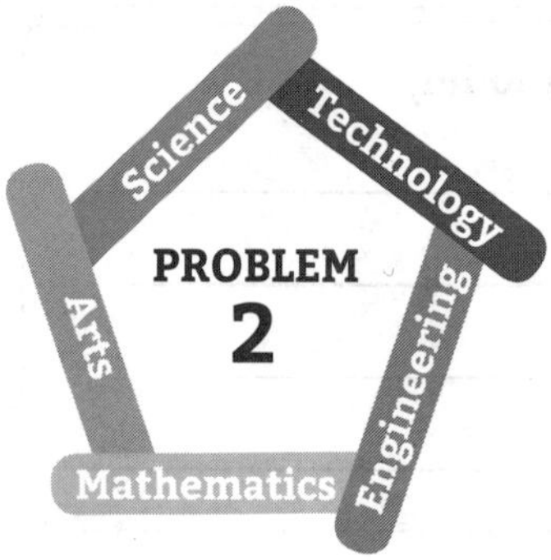


Harmeet read that doctors use stethoscope to listen to their patient's heartbeat. He decided to collect information on stethoscope and construct a small stethoscope.

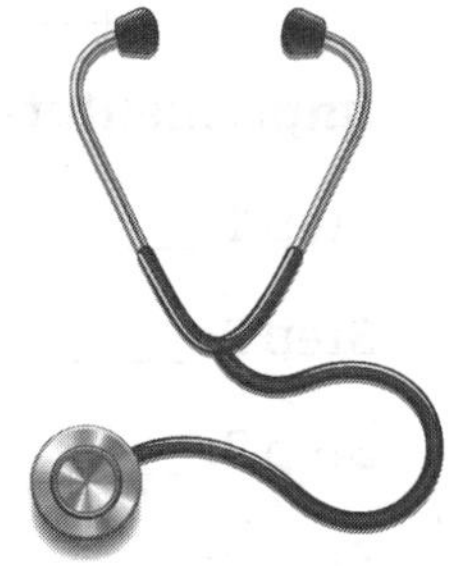

Help Harmeet design and construct a simple stethoscope and use the same to listen to your friend's heartbeat.

**Statement of the problem:**

______________________________________________

______________________________________________

______________________________________________

______________________________________________

______________________________________________

______________________________________________

______________________________________________

______________________________________________

**Research tips:**

1. Stethoscope
2. Heartbeat
3. Chest piece
4. Earpieces
5. Tube of a stethoscope

**Gather information relevant for this problem.**

1. ______________________________________________
______________________________________________
2. ______________________________________________
______________________________________________
3. ______________________________________________
______________________________________________
4. ______________________________________________
______________________________________________

**Draw/Sketch your design.**

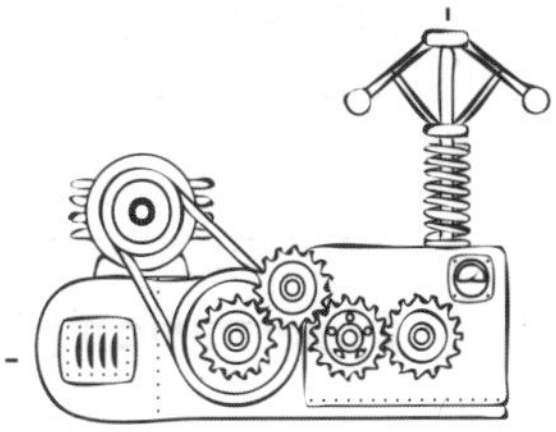

**Materials required:**

______________________________

______________________________

______________________________

______________________________

______________________________

**Construction (Write down the steps to build your design):**

1. ______________________________

   ______________________________

2. ______________________________

   ______________________________

3. ______________________________

   ______________________________

4. ______________________________

   ______________________________

**Implementation of the prototype (Try out your model):**

Step 1: ______________________________

Step 2: ______________________________

Step 3: ______________________________

Step 4: ______________________________

**Observation (What worked? What did not work?):**

______________________________

______________________________

______________________________

______________________________

______________________________

**Scope for improvement (How can you make it better?):**

**STEAM Vocabulary**

**Construction:** The way in which a thing is built or put together

**Implementation:** Trying out/carrying out/experimenting

**Prototype:** A working model of a new product/new version of an old product

**Scope:** Possibility

# Assessment 1

**CHAPTERS 1-4**
(Maximum Marks = 25)

**A. Choose the correct option for each of the following.** **(7 × 1 = 7)**

1. Which of the following parts support a plant below the ground?
   (a) Leaves (b) Stems (c) Roots (d) Flowers
2. Which of the following has its seeds outside the fruit?
   (a) Strawberry (b) Jackfruit (c) Guava (d) Apple
3. Which of the following is the breathing organ in cockroaches and butterflies?
   (a) Nose (b) Stomata (c) Mouth (d) Air holes
4. Which of the following is not a body part used for movement in living things?
   (a) Gills (b) Wings (c) Fins (d) Legs
5. Identify the bird that has a long and pointed straw-like beak.
   (a) Eagle (b) Parrot (c) Hummingbird (d) Pigeon
6. Identify the animal that uses 'sucking' as a method of feeding.
   (a) Rabbit (b) Lizard (c) Squirrel (d) Butterfly
7. Which of the following is a herbivore?
   (a) Crocodile (b) Wolf (c) Giraffe (d) Dog

**B. State whether the following statements are true (T) or false (F).** **(6 × 1 = 6)**

1. All the green plants prepare their own food. ☐
2. New plants grow from seeds. ☐
3. Birds eat only grains, seeds and fruits. ☐
4. All non-living things are man-made. ☐
5. Duck and swan both have webbed feet. ☐
6. Elephants use their trunk only for lifting logs of wood. ☐

**C. Replace the underlined word in each of the following sentences with the correct word.** **(6 × 1 = 6)**

1. The <u>leaves</u> become fruits that contain one or more seeds.
2. Germination of seeds is an example of <u>breathing</u> in living things.
3. Rocks are <u>man-made things</u> found in nature.
4. <u>Flight</u> feathers help in keeping the bird's body warm.
5. <u>Scratching</u> birds use their feet for walking in shallow water.
6. <u>Herbivores</u> are the animals that eat the flesh of other animals.

**D. Answer each of the following questions in one word.** **(6 × 1 = 6)**

1. Name the process of the growth of a seed into a new plant.
2. What are the small openings on the underside of the leaves called?

3. Name the place where birds live with their young ones.
4. What is the partially chewed and swallowed food called?
5. Name the chain formed when one organism is eaten by another organism as food.
6. What are the sharp and curved claws of flesh-eating birds called?

# Assessment 2

**CHAPTERS 5-7**

(Maximum Marks = 25)

**A. Pick the odd one out from each of the following groups of words. (7 × 1 = 7)**

| | | | | |
|---|---|---|---|---|
| 1. | Bandage | Cotton | Toys | Scissors |
| 2. | Plug | Wound | Switches | Wires |
| 3. | Wool | Nylon | Silk | Jute |
| 4. | Kennel | Doors | Windows | Walls |
| 5. | Cell | Tissue | Organ | Exercise |
| 6. | Respiratory | Circulatory | Skeletal | Tissue |
| 7. | Backbone | Joint | Skeleton | Brain |

**B. State whether the following statements are true (T) or false (F). (6 × 1 = 6)**

1. The food items in the kitchen should always be kept uncovered. ☐
2. Natural fibres are obtained only from plants. ☐
3. We should not fly kites on an open terrace. ☐
4. We should never use a subway to cross the road. ☐
5. Exercise helps the body to grow healthier. ☐
6. We breathe through our skin. ☐

**C. Fill in the blanks using correct words. (6 × 1 = 6)**

1. Playing with sharp objects may cause ____________. (a burn/an injury)
2. The air we breathe in is called ____________ air. (inhaled/exhaled)
3. Dustbins should be kept covered to keep away the ____________. (houseflies/butterflies)
4. Man-made fibres are also called ____________ fibres. (synthetic/natural)
5. All living things are made up of very small parts called ____________. (cells/tissues)
6. The ____________ system helps in producing babies. (reproductive/digestive)

**D. Answer the following questions in one word each. (6 × 1 = 6)**

1. What type of clothes protect our body from cold and keep us warm?
2. Name a material that is used to make clothes.

3. Name for the first treatment given to an injured person before taking him to a doctor.
4. Name the place where people walk on the road.
5. Name the process of breaking food into simple substances that can be used by our body.
6. Name the system that helps us to move our body parts.

# Assessment 3

**CHAPTERS 8-11**
(Maximum Marks = 25)

**A. Choose the correct option for each of the following.** **(7 × 1 = 7)**

1. Which of the following animal does not live in soil?
   (a) Scorpion (b) Earthworm (c) Ants (d) Parrot
2. The path of the Earth around the sun is known as its
   (a) rotation (b) orbit (c) revolution (d) way
3. Which of the following gas is required for breathing?
   (a) Nitrogen (b) Oxygen (c) Carbon dioxide (d) Water vapour
4. The term 'storm' is associated with
   (a) Hot weather (b) Cloudy weather (c) Windy weather (d) Rainy weather
5. The revolution of the Earth around the sun takes a time of
   (a) 24 hours (b) 364 days (c) 24 days (d) 365 ¼ days
6. Which among the following is the farthest planet from the sun?
   (a) Mercury (b) Uranus (c) Saturn (d) Neptune
7. Which among the following is a satellite?
   (a) Venus (b) Moon (c) Mars (d) Saturn

**B. State whether the following statements are true (T) or false (F).** **(6 × 1 = 6)**

1. The water that is present inside the soil is called moisture. ☐
2. Earth is always stationary. ☐
3. Water is present in the air in the form of water vapour. ☐
4. Carbon dioxide is required for burning things. ☐
5. There are nine planets in our solar system. ☐
6. Orion is a constellation. ☐

**C. Replace the underlined word in each of the following sentences with the correct word.** **(6 × 1 = 6)**

1. <u>Sandy</u> soil holds a lot of water and is sticky.
2. <u>Gravel</u> makes the soil rich and fertile.

3. Earth is flat in shape.
4. Evaporation is a process in which water vapour changes into water.
5. A strong wind is called breeze.
6. Moon gives us light and heat.

**D. Answer each of the following questions in one word.** **(6 × 1 = 6)**

1. Name the uppermost layer of the Earth's surface on which plants grow.
2. Name the type of soil good for growing cactus and other desert plants.
3. What is the blanket of air around the Earth called?
4. What portion of the Earth is covered with water?
5. What is the day-to-day condition of a particular place called?
6. What is a group of stars forming certain patterns in the night sky called?

# Assessment 4

**CHAPTERS 12-14**
(Maximum Marks = 25)

**A. Pick the odd one out from each of the following group of words.** **(7 × 1 = 7)**

| | | | | |
|---|---|---|---|---|
| 1. | Air | Water | Milk | Ink |
| 2. | Pencil | Book | Honey | Eggs |
| 3. | Water | Ice | Steam | Milk |
| 4. | Sun | Table | Bulb | Lantern |
| 5. | Squeezing | Pressing | Pushing | Laughing |
| 6. | Measuring jar | Clock | Calendar | Watch |
| 7. | Centimetre | Metre | Litre | Kilometre |

**B. Circle YES if the statement is correct and NO if the statement is wrong.** **(6 × 1 = 6)**

1. Do solids move by themselves? YES NO
2. Can we change steam into water? YES NO
3. Frictional force slows down the movement of an object. YES NO
4. Unpleasant sounds are called music. YES NO
5. The unit litre is used to measure mass. YES NO
6. Common units for measuring length are metre and centimetre. YES NO

**C. Fill in the blanks using the correct words.** **(6 × 1 = 6)**

1. ______________ exists in three different forms. (Milk/Water)
2. Ice is the ______________ form of water. (solid/liquid)
3. ______________ is required for a shadow to form. (Light/Water)

4. The shadow of an object is the shortest during ____________. (morning/noon)
5. The amount of liquid a container can hold is called its ____________. (capacity/mass)
6. Mass is commonly measured in ____________. (litre/kilogram)

**D. Answer each of the following questions in one word each.** **(6 × 1 = 6)**

1. Name the process in which a solid turns into liquid on heating.
2. What are the sounds pleasant to our ears called?
3. What are the objects that give out light called?
4. Name a device that can be used to measure the length of a pencil.
5. Name the unit that measures from the elbow to the tip of the middle finger.
6. Name the quantity measured using the unit hour.

# Comprehensive Assessment 1

**CHAPTERS 1–7**
(Maximum Marks = 50)

**A. Answer the following questions in one word each.** **(10 × 1 = 10)**

1. Name the main root that grows from the base of the stem into the soil.
2. By which other name do we know the underground path used to cross the roads?
3. Which rules are to be followed everywhere?
4. Name the animals that help in decaying the remains of dead plants and animals.
5. What type of fibres are obtained from plants?
6. Name the organ that removes wastes from the blood.
7. Which bird uses its beak as a needle to sew leaves together using wool and thread?
8. What is the other name for plant-eating animals?
9. What are the animals that eat both plants and the flesh of other animals called?
10. Which system is made up of ribs, skull, backbone and joints?

**B. In each of the following questions, two choices are correct. Identify the correct choices.** **(9 × 2 = 18)**

1. Imagine that you have planted different types of plants in your garden. Which one of the following you would not do?
   (a) Watering the plants regularly.
   (b) Walking over the soft plants and lawns.
   (c) Adding manure to them.
   (d) Plucking the flowers and uprooting the plants.
   (e) Trimming the plants every now and then.
   (f) Protecting the plants from grazing animals.

2. One of your friends fell down from the stairs and his knee is bleeding. How would you react to this situation?
   (a) You would call your other friends and surround the boy.
   (b) You would try to comfort him.
   (c) You would try to touch the wound.
   (d) You would call an adult immediately.
   (e) You would try to lift him.
   (f) You would make fun of him.
3. Which of the following you should do to keep your house clean?
   (a) I scatter my toys on the floor.
   (b) I throw the garbage outside the dustbin.
   (c) I keep my room clean.
   (d) I keep my surroundings clean.
   (e) I bang the doors often.
   (f) I play cricket in my drawing room.
4. A good and comfortable house should have
   (a) spacious rooms.
   (b) garbage everywhere.
   (c) mosquitoes and other insects.
   (d) wire netting for windows.
   (e) unclean surroundings.
   (f) muddy flooring.
5. Which of the following is not advisable to treat a wound?
   (a) Try to press the wound.
   (b) Wash the area with clean water.
   (c) Wipe and apply an antiseptic cream.
   (d) Tie a clean cloth or bandage over the wound.
   (e) Try to prick the wound.
   (f) Immediately call an adult or go to a doctor.
6. Identify two words that convey any feeling of living beings.
   (a) Smelling
   (b) Eating
   (c) Pain
   (d) Hearing
   (e) Touch
   (f) Running
7. Identify the aquatic birds from the following.
   (a) Swan
   (b) Duck
   (c) Crow
   (d) Parrot
   (e) Woodpecker
   (f) Owl
8. Which of the following animals gnaw their food?
   (a) Horse
   (b) Leech
   (c) Mosquito
   (d) Squirrel
   (e) Rat
   (f) Frog
9. The nervous system controls the whole body and includes
   (a) Brain
   (b) Blood vessels
   (c) Heart
   (d) Spinal cord
   (e) Blood
   (f) Lungs

C. **Answer the following questions briefly.** **(2 × 3 = 6)**

1. List down the requirements of a house to have a comfortable living.
2. Briefly explain food chain with the help of an example.

D. **Answer the following questions.** **(4 × 4 = 16)**

1. What is a leaf? Draw a leaf and label its parts.
2. Explain any four features of living things.
3. What are the various kinds of beaks that birds have? Mention each type with relevant examples.
4. List down any four safety rules that should be followed on the road.

# Comprehensive Assessment 2

**CHAPTERS 8–14**
(Maximum Marks = 50)

A. **Answer the following questions in one word each.** **(10 × 1 = 10)**

1. Which type of soil is rich in nutrients?
2. Which process describes the continuous movement of water between the land, water bodies and air?
3. Name the process in which a liquid turns into solid on cooling.
4. Name the quantity that helps us to measure how heavy or light an object is.
5. Name the imaginary line on which the Earth spins.
6. Which is the largest planet in the solar system?
7. What are the large pits seen on the surface of the moon called?
8. What are the objects that do not give out their own light called?
9. What do you call the push or pull applied on a body?
10. What do you call the dark patch of formed when the path of light is blocked by an object?

B. **In each of the following questions, two choices are correct. Identify the correct choices.** **(9 × 2 = 18)**

1. Why do potters use clayey soil for making pots and other articles?
   (a) Because it is dark in colour
   (b) Because it is a mixture of sand and humus
   (c) Because it is very smooth and sticky
   (d) Because it is found in deserts
   (e) Because it is made up of small and big stones
   (f) Because it holds a lot of water
2. Which of the following are associated with hot weather?
   (a) Rays of sun covered by clouds (b) Bright day
   (c) Woollen clothes (d) Noisy wind
   (e) Cotton clothes (f) Wet surroundings

3. Which of the following are the characteristic features of gases?
   (a) Fixed shape
   (b) No shape
   (c) Occupies fixed space
   (d) Do not flow by themselves
   (e) Flow in all directions
   (f) Take the shape of a container
4. Which of the following statements are true about the movement of the Earth?
   (a) Both rotation and revolution happen at the same time.
   (b) Rotation takes 24 hours and revolution takes 365 ¼ days.
   (c) Rotation takes 24 days and revolution takes 365 ¼ days.
   (d) Rotation leads to the formation of seasons on the Earth.
   (e) Revolution is the spinning of the Earth on a fixed point.
   (f) Rotation and revolution happens on an imaginary orbit.
5. Which of the following sounds can be considered unpleasant?
   (a) Car honking
   (b) Guitar played by an artist
   (c) A child crying
   (d) Professional singing
   (e) Birds chirping
   (f) An artist playing flute
6. Rotation takes place on an imaginary axis and revolution happens on an imaginary orbit
   (a) Venus
   (b) Orion
   (c) Ursa Major
   (d) Earth
   (e) Sun
   (f) None of these
7. Which of the following are a must to form a shadow?
   (a) Object
   (b) Force
   (c) Dark cloth
   (d) Sound
   (e) Light source
   (f) Sun
8. Which of the following are used to measure capacity?
   (a) kilogram
   (b) litre
   (c) metre
   (d) gram
   (e) millilitre
   (f) centimetre
9. Which of the following are time-measuring devices?
   (a) Wall clock
   (b) Beam balance
   (c) Wristwatch
   (d) Measuring tape
   (e) Measuring jar
   (f) Ruler

**C. Answer the following questions briefly.** **(2 × 3 = 6)**

1. What are the phases of moon?
2. Write a note on the rotation and revolution of the Earth.

**D. Answer the following questions.** **(4 × 4 = 16)**

1. How do rocks become soil? Explain.
2. Explain water cycle with the help of a diagram.
3. What is force? Also list down the various effects of force.
4. Name the different ways used for measuring length in early days. Justify with an example the disadvantage of early approach of length measurement in comparison with the modern devices.

# My Green Patch

We have some wooden boxes hanging in the garden with seeds for birds. Birds will nest on those boxes, and eat all the small pests and bugs which can harm the plants.
Great idea! I know some of the birds that eat pests like snails and slugs.
This is so interesting! Give us some more tips.
Make a small compost pit. You do not need a large area. You can even use a small bin where you can dump all the remains of dead plants, fallen leaves, cut grass, etc.
Can we add vegetable and fruit peels from the kitchen?
Yes, of course! But please do not add oils, dairy waste, etc. After some days, you can use this compost as manure for your plants.

Do not pluck flowers from the garden. The flowers will attract butterflies and bees, and help in pollination.
Great ideas, Amrita! You use all environment-friendly ways to maintain your garden.
We can even collect rainwater in the containers. Close the container with a lid once it stops raining so that mosquitoes do not lay eggs inside them. Use this water for watering your plants.
Thank you for these useful tips, Amrita! Now, we are eager to have our own 'Green Patch'.

# Skills You Need

### TRAVEL AND TOURISM

People travel for different reasons, such as for business purposes and visiting family and friends. When people travel for pleasure, they are called tourists. Tourism is the business of encouraging and supporting tourists. Most of the times, people go on vacation because they want a break from their everyday lives or to experience a different climate. Many people enjoy learning about different cultures tasting new cuisines, and observing different lifestyles.

## Types of Tourisms

There are different types of tourisms. Some of them are:

**Business tourism**

Travel to attend a business cevents

**Nature Tourism**

Travel to enjoy a natural setting or wildlife

**Cultural Tourism**

Travel to experience the history, folklore and culture of the people

**Science tourism**

Travel that involves visiting and exploring scientific landmarks, including museums, laboratories, observatories and universities

### TOURISM AND ENVIRONMENT

Many countries promote tourism by developing areas that will attract visitors. This development sometimes causes concern from environmentalists and local residents.

Some places are so popular with tourists that they are in danger of being damaged. Noise and traffic pollution, littering and the erosion of footpaths are just some of the environmental problems caused by tourists. For this reason, all popular tourist spots need to be managed carefully.

**Ecotourism** means responsible travel to natural areas that conserves the environment, sustains the well-being of the local people and involves education.

### Career Exploration

- Airlines Staff
- Tourist Guide
- Travel Officer
- Travel Counselor
- Travel Agent
- Science Tourist Guide

## TOURISM CLASS

### To be a Responsible Tourist/Tourist Guide

When we travel, we should take responsibility of our own waste. In many countries, garbage bins are given standard colours for different types of waste. In India, the most common three colours used for garbage bins are blue, green and black.

**Green bins** are for organic wastes like cooked food, vegetables/fruit peels, eggs, coconut shells, tea bags, etc. You can also place the garden waste like leaves, twigs, flowers, etc. into green bins.

**Blue bins** are for the left overs. This includes plastic covers, bottles, cups, wrappers, newspapers, pizza boxes, paper cups/plates, foil paper, rubber, thermocol, etc.

**Black bins** are for the harmful wastes like blades, bandages, broken thermometer, batteries, expired medicines, etc.

### Try it!

Find out the colour codes given to garbage bins in the country you wish to travel.

# Happiness Activity Sheets

## I AM GRATEFUL FOR MY BODY

Our body is our home. Not just today, but for the rest of our lives. It is important to look after our body, to help us to stay healthy for as long as we can. We should be grateful for our body.

Every time you see yourself in the mirror, practise a whole-body gratitude scan.

Thank you, ears. You help me listen to sounds all around.

Thank you, brain. You help me by generating all creative thoughts.

Thank you, eyes. You help me see the beauty of this world.

Thank you, mouth. You help me speak my mind.

Thank you, hands. You help me to write and draw.

Thank you, stomach. You help me digest my food.

Thank you, heart. You keep me alive.

Thank you, legs. You carry me around. You help me walk, jump and run.

**Are you aware of yourself?**

My body is ________ and ________

It helps me ________

## How mindful are you?

Do you know there are little habits we mindlessly practise every day without even realizing the negative effect they have on our body? Reflect and write any such five habits.

How would you rectify these bad habits so as to keep your body healthy?

## What about a Role Play!

Arrange your class into groups. Let each student play a body part. What would do to take care of yourself? Write your script in the post-it provided alongside. Start your role play!

# Vernacular Names

**Elephant** • Assamese: *Haati* • Bengali: *Hati* • Hindi: *Haati* • Kannada: *Aane* • Meiteilon: *Samu* • Marathi: *Hatti* • Malayalam: *Ana* • Mizo: *Sai* • Tamil: *Yanai* • Telugu: *Enugu* • Urdu: *Haati*

**Ginger** • Assamese: *Ada* • Bengali: *Ada* • Hindi: *Adrak* • Kannada: *Shunti* • Meiteilon: *Shing* • Marathi: *Ale* • Malayalam: *Inci* • Mizo: *Sawh thing* • Tamil: *Inji* • Telugu: *Allam* • Urdu: *Adrak*

**Giraffe** • Assamese: *Giraph* • Hindi: *Jiraaf* • Kannada: *Jiraphe* • Malayalam: *Jiraph* • Marathi: *Jhirapha* • Mizo: *Sanghawngsei* • Tamil: *Ottakaccivinki* • Telugu: *Jhiraphi* • Urdu: *Ziraafa*

**Jupiter** • Assamese: *Brihospoti* • Bengali: *Brihaspati* • Hindi: *Brhaspati* • Kannada: *Guru* • Malayalam: *Vyalam* • Marathi: *Guru* • Mizo: *Hrangchhuana* •Tamil: *Viyalan* • Telugu: *Brhaspathi* • Urdu: *Mushtari Siyarah*

**Leech** • Assamese: *Junke* • Bengali: *Jnoke* • Hindi: *Jonk* • Kannada: *Lic* • Meiteilon: *Kak-phei* • Marathi: *Jalu* • Malayalam: *Atta* • Mizo: *Vangvat seila* • Tamil: *Attai* • Telugu: *Jalaga* • Urdu: *Jonk*

**Mercury** • Assamese: *Budh* • Bengali: *Budha* • Hindi: *Budh* • Kannada: *Padarasa graha* • Marathi: *Para graha* • Malayalam: *Merkkuri graham* • Mizo: *Tangkaraw tui* • Tamil: *Putan kirakam* • Telugu: *Padarasam graham* • Urdu: *Parah Sayarah*

**Neptune** • Assamese: *Nepcun* • Hindi: *Varun* • Kannada: *Nepcun* • Marathi: *Nepacyuna* • Malayalam: *Neprryun* • Tamil: *Neptiyun* • Telugu: *Neptyun* • Urdu: *Neptune Sayarah*

**Potato** • Assamese: *Alu* • Bengali: *Alu* • Hindi: *Aloo* • Kannada: *Alugedde* • Meiteilon: *Aloo* • Marathi: *Batata* • Malayalam: *Urulakkilann* • Mizo: *Alu* • Tamil: *Urulaikkilanku* • Telugu: *Bangaladumpa* • Urdu: *Alu*

**Rat** • Assamese: *Endura* • Bengali: *Eendur* • Hindi: *Chooha* • Kannada: *Eli* • Meiteilon: *Uchee* • Marathi: *Undira* • Malayalam: *Eli* • Mizo: *Sazu* • Tamil: *Eli* • Telugu: *Eluka* • Urdu: *Chooha*

**Saturn** • Assamese: *Shoni* • Bengali: *Shoni* • Hindi: *Shani* • Kannada: *Sani* • Marathi: *Sani* • Malayalam: *Sani* • Tamil: *Sani* • Telugu: *Mamidi* • Urdu: *Kewan Sayarah*

**Venus** • Assamese: *Shukro* • Bengali: *Shukro* • Hindi: *Sukra* • Kannada: *Sukra* • Malayalam: *Sukran* • Marathi: *Sukra* • Mizo: *Chawngmawii* • Tamil: *Velli* • Telugu: *Sukrudu* • Urdu: *Zuhra Sayarah*

**Wolf** • Assamese: *Kuku neciya bagh* • Bengali: *Nekre* • Hindi: *Bhediya* • Kannada: *Tola* • Meiteilon: *Lamhui* • Marathi: *Landaga* • Malayalam: *Cennaya* • Mizo: *Chinghnia* • Tamil: *Onay* • Telugu: *Todelu* • Urdu: *Bheria*

---

What do you call these plants and animals in your language? Share the names with us at **schoolsupport@harpercollins.co.in**